# CAROLING THROUGH THE PSALMS

## ~For Comfort and Joy~

Adapted by L. L. Larkins

Names: Larkins, L. L.
Title: Caroling Through The Psalms / adapted for singing and dramatic recitation by L. L. Larkins.
Description: Littleton, Colorado : Capture Books, [2016] | Caroling Through the Psalms; Abridged from Psalm Hymns Volume 1 and Volume 2| Words only. | Includes bibliographical references: no index.
Identifiers: ISBN 13: 978-0-9978976-1-6 | ISBN-10: 0-9978976-1-9
| ISBN 13: 978-0-9978976-0-9 (ebook)
Subjects: LCSH: Psalms (Music) | Hymns, English, American. | Bible--Meditations. | Worship in the Bible.
Classification: LCC BS1424 .L37 2016 | LCC BS1424 (ebook) | DDC 223/.2052--dc23
ART060000 Art: Performance | SEL016000 Self-Help | EDU017000 Education | Christmas Novelty
Song Resource | Philosophy & Religion | Spirituality: Sacred Texts

Special appreciation goes to the writers of the ESV, Holman, The New Jerusalem Bible, The King James and New King James, The Message, NASB, NIV, The New Living Translation Bibles. All these versions and translations were utilized by the author in the adaption of these psalm lyrics.

# TABLE OF CONTENTS

# PSALM 15

*(A psalm of David.*
*Teaching those who do not slander and gossip may enter)*
*TUNE: STILL, STILL, STILL*
Orig. Folk Tune (authorship unknown) from Salzburg

Who~ may adore the LORD of Lords on high?

    Who may enter into His Presence?

On His holy hill of Defense?

Those~ whose~ feet lead on to blameless lives.


Do~ what is right, speak truth to bring in light

    Never harm a neighbor in gossip,

And refuse to speak in slander

Do~ distain all those who bring demise.


Who~ may~ come to honor the King supreme?

    Those who honor faithful mentors

Loving the LORD, in truth, will enter

Do~ not~ curse your friends in high esteem.


Who~ may~ come to worship the KING of Kings?

    Those who lend not charging interest,

Not being bribed to slight the innocent.

These~ will~ stand forever and serene.

# PSALM 23

(The closeness of the LORD)

*TUNE: AWAY IN A MANGER*
Mueller, James R. Murray (1887)
*Alternate Tunes:* The Cradle Song/Away in a Manger
William J. Kirkpatrick (1895)
*IMMORTAL, INVISIBLE, GOD ONLY WISE*
St. Denio*"A Hundred Years from Now"* (1839)
French Carol: Noël Nouvelet SING WE ALL NOEL

The LORD *is* my shepherd;

He meets every need;

He makes me lie down in

Green meadows of peace;

He leads me beside the

Still waters for drink.

And there He restores my soul;

There He gives strength.


My Shepherd leads over

The paths we must take

In love and in righteousness

For His name's sake.

Although we pass through

Vales of shadowy death,

I fear, there, no evil

No perishing breath.

For You are beside me;

Your rod and Your staff

Bring comfort and guide me

To rest and to laugh.

You spread me a feast

In the presence of foes;

Your oil anoints me,

My cup overflows.


My cup spills with plenty,

Restoring my soul.

And mercies will follow me;

Goodness will grow.

Through all of the days of my life

I will dwell

Forever, oh LORD, in

Your home to live well.

# PSALM 27

(A Lament of David of fear, Confidence in the LORD)
*TUNE: IMMORTAL, INVISIBLE*
Orig. St. Denio, Welsh melody, from Canaidau y Cyssegr,
by John Roberts (1839)
*Alternate Tunes: I WONDER AS I WANDER,*
John Jacob Niles (1933)
*AWAY IN A MANAGER*
Mueller, James R. Murray (1887)

The LORD is my Light and my constant Estate

    Then whom shall I fear when His Stronghold is safe?

Though evil advances against me for ill

    To slander, devour me all will be well.


My rivals and enemies stumble and fall.

    Though armies besiege me, I fear none at all;

Though warriors may shake down a valiant defense,

    Then yes, God alone is my sheer confidence.


This one thing I seek, and I ask from the LORD,

    To hold my insurance for life at the Source

To gaze on His beauty to seek His embrace

    For here in my trouble He will keep me safe.


Though hiding in shelters in His sacred tents

    He sets me on high over enemy angst.

My head is exalted, and here I will sing

    In shouts to my Savior, in songs to my King.

Be merciful, hear me and answer my cry.

      I speak to my heart, "Seek His face now or die;"

Your face, LORD, I seek. Do not hide it in rage,

      Now don't turn or leave me, O Helper who saves!

 

And yes, though a father and mother take leave,

      The LORD will receive me; to Him  I will cleave.

Now, lead me in honesty, spite all my foes.

      I wait for the LORD, O take heart, He is close!

# PSALM 29

(A Praise Hymn for the Voice of the LORD)
*TUNE: ANGELS WE HAVE HEARD ON HIGH*
Orig. Languedoc, France. Unknown author. Public Domain.
*Alternate Tune:* French carol: Bring a Torch, Jeanette Isabella
Hark! The Herald Angels Sing (done by combining two verses and omitting chorus)

All you angels, heavenly beings,

Sons of heroes, sons of kings:

To the LORD on high ascribe

Glory due His name on high!

    Glo~~~~~~~~ria

    Strength in full resplendence!

    Glo~~~~~~~~ria

    In His Holy Presence!

Fr. Carol to start.

(if using Fr. Carol, change last line to:

    In His Holiness)

YAHWEH's voice is far revered,

High above the atmosphere.

God in glory sends His voice

Decibels are thunderous!

    Glo~~~~~~~~ria

    Strength in full resplendence!

    Glo~~~~~~~~ria

    In His Holy Presence! (Holiness)

(Repeat these two lines if

Singing, Hark the Herald Angels Sing)

Vocals of the LORD will shower       (start here: Angels We Have Heard)

In their splendor, over power!

Breaking trees of Lebanon,

Cedars scattered in a song!

    Glo~~~~~~~~ria

    Strength in full resplendence!

    Glo~~~~~~~~ria

    In His Holy Presence!


Lebanon skips like a calf,

And Mount Hermon, too, will laugh.

Young and wild Sirion,

Soon will laugh for old is young.

    Glo~~~~~~~~ria

    Strength in full resplendence!

    Glo~~~~~~~~ria

    In His Holy Presence!

May modulate key or:

Sing: Hark the Herald Angels Sing

Do you hear God's flashing voice?

It will shake the wilderness,

Flames of fire when it pours,

When His voice on Kadesh roars!

    Glo~~~~~~~~ria

    Strength in full resplendence!

    Glo~~~~~~~~ria

    In His Holy Presence! (Holiness)

Vocals of the LORD shall make

Deer give birth and forests shake.

It will make the woodlands ache;

It will make the live oaks break.

    Glo~~~~~~~ria

    Strength in full resplendence!

    Glo~~~~~~~ria

    In His Holy Presence!


In His temple, hear them cry,          Fr. Carol

"Glory! Adoni, on high!"

At the flood the LORD was King,

When the flood rose, He gave strength.

    Glo~~~~~~~ria

    Strength in full resplendence!

    Glo~~~~~~~ria

    In His Holiness!


Adoni, enthroned in peace,          Fr. Carol

Giving all His people strength;

King forever, He is wise,

Blessing them with peaceful ties.

    Glo~~~~~~~ria

    Strength in full resplendence!

    Glo~~~~~~~ria

    In His Holiness!

# PSALM 35

*A Nishmat (breath) of David. An Imprecatory Psalm*
*TUNE: GOD REST YE MERRY GENTLEMEN*
Orig. English Roud Folk Song (1833)
Tune is also used with Psalm 147
*Alternate Tune:* French carol: Les Rois Mages

Contend, oh LORD,

Contend with those

Who fight and strive with me!

In competition, take my part,

Take up a shield, I plea!

Arise and bring Your armor here.

Arise and come for aid.

Oh, brandish Your javelin and spear, and make a play!

Pressing in pursuit,

We shout Your saving grace!

May those who seek

To end my life

Be quit and put to shame;

May those who plot my ruining

Be turned back in dismay;

Their weight be insignificant

And light as chaff on wind.

May the Almighty be in hot pursuit, in angel's breath;

May their path be dark

In slippery torment.

Since, without cause,

They hid their nets

For me and dug a pit,

May ruin overtake them by

Surprise of nets they hid.

And when they fall into their pit in joy

My soul will leap

To the LORD of Salvation, exclaiming, I will sing,

"Who is like our LORD and

Leader, who competes?

You rescue poor

From those who are

Too strong and fully armed;

You rescue poor and needy from

The robbers who do harm."

When ruthless witnesses come forth

To question me on things

Having nothing to do with me, repaying bad for good,

They abandon me as lost,

and in my grief!

I fasted humble

Prayers for them when

Their loved one grew ill.

And, when my prayers returned to me

Unanswered, I was still.

I mourned as for my own dear friend,

And bowed in weeping grief

As bereaved for my brother or my mother, was my grief.

Why then, when I stumbled,

They appeared in glee?


Assailants circled,

All against

in opposition spoke,

Without my knowledge, slandered me;

Maliciously, they joked

Like godless creatures gnashing teeth,

Without a cause, they breathe;

Oh how long will You mildly look on their raving words?

Oh LORD, lift me from these lions'

Dreadful claws!

I will give thanks

To You, oh LORD,

In great community;

Among the masses I will praise You.

Don't let enemies

Come gloat or hate maliciously

On me without a cause,

Winking eyes, speaking peace but playing games for their increase,

Making accusations in

Their gloating sprees.


They point their hand

Against the quiet ones

Who live on land.

They sneer at me and say, "Aha!

Our witnesses will stand."

LORD, have You seen this? Are You mute?

Oh, don't go far abroad!

Now, awake! to contend for me and rise to my defense!

Vindicate me in Your

Righteousness, my God.

May all who gloat

In my distress

Be bowed and put to shame;

May those who lord it over me

Wear rags and bitter chains.

May those delighting in my vindication

shout for joy

And in gladness say, "Be exalted, LORD, for You delight

In the comforts of Your servant,

You are right!"

# PSALM 49

(Declaring the foolishness of trusting in riches)
*TUNE: IT CAME UPON A MIDNIGHT CLEAR #/4*
*"CAROL,"* Richard S. Willis (1850)
*Alternate tunes: "NOEL,"* Arthur S. Sullivan (1871)
ALAS! AND DID MY SAVIOR BLEED 4/4 (At the Cross, At the Cross)
Isaac Watts, (1740) Ralph Erskine Hudson (1860)

Hear this, all nations of the world;

You great and small in heart,

You rich and poor together hear

My wisdom on the harp!

My meditation shall be clear

As understanding prose:

The proverb and the riddle sing

As I explain them both:


Why should I fear when danger comes

Confounded enemies,

The ones who put their trust in wealth

And boast iniquities?

For no-one's assets can redeem

The price of human life;

Each costly soul is ransomed by

Our God who set His price.

What could we pay that God would trade

To let us out-live time?

Immortal like, enjoying life

In rich estates sublime?

For one can see that wise ones die,

And fools, they all pass away.

They leave their wealth to other hands.

Their homes become their graves.

Estates are named to flatter pride

Of pompous heirs below

But generations pass on by

Those silent wealthy bones.

Despite one's wealth, the flesh won't last;

For humans die like herds;

There goes the path of the arrogant,

And those who follow their words.

As sheep are destined for the pit,

Decay will shepherd the proud.

Yet, morning casts its waking light

Where those of virtue are crowned.

Conceited forms will waste away

Far from their lofty estates.

But God will fully redeem my life

From powers of the grave.

The LORD will take me, I'm not afraid;

And neither should you fear!

For some get rich, and homes increase,

But when they die, it's clear:

A soul takes nothing to the grave,

Releasing wealth and pride.

Though self-made men are lavished praise,

Their souls will never see light.

# PSALM 53

(Declaring Salvation from the foolish and wicked)
*TUNE: I HEARD THE BELLS ON CHRISTMAS DAY*
John Baptiste Calkin (1848)
To be sung antiphonally by a leader and a chorus.
*Alternate Tune:* I HEARD THE BELLS ON CHRISTMAS DAY
Joseph Mainzer (1845)

The fool repeats down in his heart,

"There is no God to disregard."

These fools are vile, their ways corrupt;

And no-one gives an afterthought.


Our God is looking down from heaven

To see if any understand,

Of human kind, do any plan

To seek their true Designer's hand?


See, everyone has turned away,

Corrupted, they have disobeyed;

No-one does good, not even one.

Do wicked see they are undone?


Will evil people never dread?

They eat my people's life like bread!

They never think to call on God.

When terror comes, then comes a rod.

The wicked, overwhelmed with dread,

   Turned back when God drew near, and fled.

He scattered those betrayers' bones

   Who violated you alone.

Oh, make salvation come of Zion,

   And Israel benefit on high!

When God restores our joy to laugh,

   Let Jacob shout on his behalf!

# PSALM 55

*(For the director of music. With stringed instruments.*
*A* Maskil *and Lament of David.)*
*TUNE: SILENT NIGHT*
Franz Xaver Gruber (1818)

Hear, oh God, Hear my cry!

   Do not turn from my sigh;

Hear and answer my troubled thoughts.

      Hear and answer me, I am distraught.

   By my enemy's sayings,

      And by his meaningful threats.


Vicious degrees of suffering,

   He assails, in sweeping wails!

Now, I languish in terrible death

      Anguish follows me, fear has beset.

   Horror! Trembling claims me.

      Oh, for the wings of a dove!

Fly away, Far away,

    I would fly, find a place.

In the desert, I'd stay in a nest,

        Sheltered safe from the tempest in chase

Hurry up to my shelter,

        From a tumultuous storm.


Oh LORD, confuse their wicked ruse,

    For I see violent streets.

There is strife in the city I love.

        Day and night they are prowling its walls;

    Malice and menacing handshakes

        Willing to kill and destroy.


If it were an enemy's rage

    I'd endure, I'd endure;

Given a foe was arising, I'd hide.

        Could this be a companion I liked?

    You, were my partner and close friend!

        Someone I always enjoyed.

Walking about, all through God's house

    Fellowshipping confidents

All the worshipers, who were our friends,

      Allies always, without a pretense.

    Oh, may death appear frightening!

        Let them go visit the dead!


As for my part, I'm calling to God;

    Watch the LORD save me now!

I am bellowing morning and night;

       In distress, though He's hearing my voice.

    Quickly coming to rescue,

      Saving me from battle cries.


Many oppose him, though He knows,

    Yet my God, stays the same!

Never ending, enthroned of old,

     He will hear and will humble the bold,

Those who live without fearing,

      Fear this, my God on His throne!

My old friend tackled his friends;

    Breeching our covenants.

While he spoke as smooth as silk,

    War moved out in his heart of guilt,

    Words more soothing than oil,

    Yet they were drawn with a sword.


Oh, cast your cares onto the LORD

    He will never let you down!

He will keep and sustain His own;

    Cast your troubles on Him and be found.

    YAHWEH cares for the righteous,

    You too may trust in my God.


God will cull the wicked souls,

    Send to pits of decay.

All the blood thirsty souls in deceit

    Will not survive many days on their feet.

    As for me, I will trust You.

    Yes, I will trust in my God.

# PSALM 61

*(A Royal Psalm of David, for the director of music. A prayer with stringed instruments.)*
*TUNE: NO ROOM, ONLY A MANGER OF HAY*
John W. Peterson (1958)
Alternate Tune: French carol: Trois Souris

Listen,

Listen, oh God, hear my cry.

Listen to my petition and sigh.

From the ends of the earth I have called,

My courage failing;


Lead me;

Onto the rock I will climb.

One God, You are my refuge on high;

For You granted me refuge before,

A stronger tower!

     I long

     To dwell here forever,

     Under Your cover and shelter,

     And to be safe in the refuge of Your wing!

For You

Listened before, and You heard

My vows, true to the sure witness heard

And strong testaments in legacy;

Your name, they clung to.


Will You

Prolong the King's living days,

Give Him more generations of praise?

May He rule on His throne evermore

in God's good presence!

Appoint

Your fullest protection!

Truth and Your faithful affection.

Then I will sing evermore to praise Your name!


Watch me

Filling my vows day by day;

Hear me singing the praise of Your name;

Watch me living a strong legacy.

My Rock is higher!

# PSALM 65

*(For the director of music. A psalm of David for Thanks and Exaltation)*
*TUNE: HARK! THE HERALD ANGELS SING!*
Felix Mendelssohn and William H. Cummings (1840)
*Alternate Tune:* French carol: PAT-A-PAN (if using this turn, ignore the verse breaks as printed.)

Praise awaits You, God, in Zion;

    Yes, to You all people come.

You, our God, will answer prayer,

    For our vows in You, repair:

When in overwhelming sins,

    You forgave our great transgressions.

Blessings rest on all You choose

    Drawing near to live with You!

In Your courts and powerhouse

    All good things do You endow.


God, You answer when we call

    God our Savior, hope of all!

Awesome deeds in righteous answers!

    to all peoples of the earth.

And to farthest seas You bring,

    Your good hope with awesome deeds!

You, Who by Your power formed

    Mountain peaks with strengthened arms.

You, Who stilled the roaring seas,

    made the nations' turmoil cease.

This whole earth is filled with awe
　　At Your wonders; at Your songs!
Where does morning light deploy;
　　Where does evening fade to joy?
You supply the land with water;
　　You enrich it for our quota.
Yes, the streams of God are filled
　　irrigating grain in fields
For all people, You provide
　　And ordain a yield for life.

Drenching furrows, and You level
　　Ridges where You soften them
With the showers of Your blessing
　　Of the crops that grow within.
So You crown the year with bounty,
　　And Your carts, they're overflowing.
There the wild grasslands bloom;
　　And the hills in glad costume,
While the meadows shout their voice
　　Covered with their flocks in joy.

# PSALM 66

(For the director of music. A psalm to sing with three groups or soloists in praise for God's miracles)

*TUNE: IT CAME UPON A MIDNIGHT CLEAR 3/4*
"Carol," Richard S. Willis (1850)
*ALTERNATE TUNES: ALAS! AND DID MY SAVIOR BLEED? 4/4*
*(AT THE CROSS, AT THE CROSS)*
Ralph E. Hudson (1885)

With joy, all earth, come shout to God;

The glories of His name!                                   (Choir 1)

Oh magnify His praises rare;

To this, our God, proclaim:


"Your acts and deeds! Your awesome feats;

And all the earth will sing,                               (Choir 2)

There's no comparing Your worth or strength!"

And, foes will bow to the sting!


Now, come and see what God has done,

His fruits to all bloodroot!

He turned the sea into dry land,

And they passed through on foot.


Come, let's rejoice for fearsome grace;

God rules supreme with power!

And, always by His watching gaze

The nations are endowed.

Come praise our God, each mother tongue,
Oh, let His praise be heard!
He has preserved our very lives
And kept our feet assured.

    You tested us, oh God, in fire
    Refined to silver bowls;
    You brought us to our prison cells
    And bent our backs with loads.

Your servants bore down our backs;
We went through fire and flood,
Yet then You brought us to a place
Of opulent reward.

    I'm coming now to worship You
    To burn my firstborn bull,
    Your temple yet awaits my vow
    My promises in full.

When times were hard, I promised vows
In sacred sacrifice;
This fat from You, I offer back,
A ram to satisfy.

The first of all belongs to You

And this is for my good

To bring into Your courts with praise

the firstfruit of my herd.

Oh, come and hear, all you who fear

This God, and what he's done

For when I cried, He soon appeared

While praise was on my tongue.

"Your acts and deeds! Your awesome feats;

And all the earth will sing,

For Who creates new birth, new wealth,

in harvest time or Spring?

If I'd preferred a heart of sin,

The LORD would not have heard

But God has surely listened well

And multiplied His word.

All praises be to God, my God,                    (All Choir)

Who did not lose my prayer!

He showered love, did not withhold,

The worth and all that's fair!

# PSALM 77

(For the director of music. For Jeduthun. A psalm of Asaph, Meditation towards Faith)

*TUNE: WHILE SHEPHERDS WATCHED THEIR FLOCKS BY NIGHT*
"Siroe," an opera by George Frederick Handel (1728)
Alternate Tune: Quittez, Pasteures (To use this tune repeat last two lines)


I cried out to our God for help;

　　I cried out, "YAHWEH, hear me!"

In my distress, with tireless hands,

　　I stretched them out for comfort

I sought the LORD all night.


I remembered You, YAHWEH, and groaned;

　　All night I meditated,

And though my fainting spirit moaned,

　　You kept my eyes from closing;

Though I could find no words.


I thought of years so long ago

　　And mused on songs I sang then;

Those songs and lyrics in the night

　　That turned my heart to "A-men."

And then my spirit asked:

"Will the LORD abandon evermore?
    Will He never show his favor?
Will He hide in fog His unfailing love
    With His promises forever?
    In wrath does pardon fail?

Then I thought, "To this I will appeal:
    The former years when the Most High
Stretched out his right compassionate hand,
    I will recall His wonders;
    Yes, I will ponder might!

Your miracles of long ago,
    Your works, I will consider
And meditate on mighty deeds.
    Your ways, oh God, are holy!
What god is great like You?"

You are God whose acts and wonderful deeds
    Were performed among all people;
You displayed Your pow'r and mighty arm
    With your strength redeeming Jacob
With heirs of Joseph too.

The waters stood to see you, God,

    The waters watched and writhed;

The very depths convulsed not of wind.

    The clouds poured down their water,

    The heavens clapped their hands!

Your arrows flashed with lightning strikes,

    And thunder was heard in the whirlwind,

 Your light lit up the world around;

    The earth, it quaked and trembled.

Your path led through the sea!

Your way led through the mighty waves,

    Though the waters held no footprints;

Where were You, God, invisible? —

    By Your hand, You led Your people,

through Moses and Aaron.

# PSALM 79

*(A psalm of Asaph, Pleading and Lament)*
*TUNE: O LITTLE TOWN OF BETHLEHEM*
Lewis Redner, "St. Louis", is the tune used most often for this carol in the U.S. but in the British Commonwealth, and in the U.S. Episcopal Church, the English hymn tune "*FOREST GREEN*" is used, as adapted by Ralph Vaughan Williams from an English folk ballad called "*THE PLOUGHBOY'S DREAM*"
Or, French carol: Lullé lullé

Oh God, the nations have invaded Your inheritance!     -O Little Town

Throughout Your temple they've defiled, Your holy silhouettes!

    Jerusalem is rubble,

        Reduced to death and shame!

           They've left Your servants' bodies for the

              Wild birds to claim!


They've poured out blood like water all around Jerusalem,

And there is no one living who can bury all the dead.

    Our neighbors' taunt and scorn us

        For their derision flies

           With those whose scorn and strong derision

              Shouts on every side.


Oh, how long will Your anger last; forever, LORD of fire?     -Lullé lullé

*How long,* I cry, will jealousy keep burning us like briar?

    Pour out Your wrath on others, (Lord)

        On those preoccupied;

           On kings and nations ignorant

              Of You for all their pride.

Cull aliens to face Your name; for they've devoured us!–

Descendants and the homes of Jacob's lands, completely crushed.

    O don't withhold compassion

        From us for ancient sins.

           In desperate need, this generation

              Begs Your great defense!


O Help us, God our Savior, to glorify Your name;           –O Little Town

Forgive our sins, atone for them, do all this for Your sake.

    Why should the nations prattle,

        "Where is the orphans' God?"

           Before our eyes, they'll realize

              That You'll avenge our blood.


O May You hear the groaning of Your own condemned to die;

With Your strong arm preserve Your servants, give them back their lives!

    Pay back into the laps of

        Our neighbors seven times

           All their contempt they hurled at you,

              LORD, when they scorned our lives.


Then we Your people, simple sheep, will give You thanks oh, LORD!   –Lullé lullé

In pastures green we'll bring You praises, Shepherd, we adore!

    From generations here and

        To generations there, we

           Will recount Your power and

              Proclaim Your full repair!

# PSALM 80

(For the director of music. A psalm of Asaph (Pleading & Lament)

TUNE: O COME, O COME EMMANUEL
"Veni Emmanuel,"15th C. plainchant: "Bone Jesu dulcis cunctis" is part of a series of
two-part tropes to the responsory Libera me.
Alternate tunes: "ST. PETERSBURG" by Dmitry Bortniansky, Aachen, (1841) and
"CONDITOR ALME SIDERUM"

Oh Shepherd, hear us, Shepherd of the flock!

You lead all Israel, Joseph with a rod.

   You sit enthroned between cherubim,

   You shine for Ephraim and Benjamin--

Oh God! Wake up Your mighty arm to save!

Light up Manasseh, shine for us always.


Oh God, restore us, save us LORD, for peace.

And make Your face shine on with Your increase.

   How long will You continue, we pray,

   To smolder over every prayer we say?

You feed Your own the wilted bread of tears;

We drink our bowl of sorrowing in fear.


A small thing of derision, You have made,

Our neighbors mock and enemies parade.

   Restore us, dear Almighty, to grace;

   Your face is welcome, shine on us, embrace!

You dug us up, our vine from Egypt's ground;

You drove out others, making us abound.

You cleared the ground for transplanting this vine,

And it took root and filled the land with wine.

    The mountains then were covered with shade,

    and mighty cedars with its colonnade.

Its branches reached as far as the great Sea,

Its shoots ran to the river's apogee.


Why have you broken down supportive walls?

For strangers steal our harvest grapes in hauls.

    And from the forest, boars ravage it,

    And insects from the fields feed on its limbs.

Return to us, Almighty God to save!

Look down from heaven, watch Your vine we pray!


The root you planted with your own right hand,

The Son, the branch, raised in Your famous plan.

    This vine is hacked, and burned with a fire;

    At your rebuke Your people are a brier.

Let your good hand rest on the man at right,

The Son of Man you raised up for Your fight.


Then we will never turn away again,

Should You revive us, we will keep Your plans.

    Restore us, LORD Almighty, to save;

    Oh make your face shine over us again.

Oh God! You shine, You send your son to save,

So shine on us, remove us from disgrace.

# PSALM 81

*(For the director of music. According to* gittith. *Of Asaph)*
*TUNE: WE THREE KINGS OF ORIENT ARE*
John Henry Hopkins, Jr., for the General Theological Seminary
(New York City, 1857)

Sing for joy to YAHWEH our strength;

Shout to Jacob's God and sing!

Start the music, strike the timbrel,

Playing the harp and strings.   Oh-oh—

Sound the shofar on that day

When the new moon finds its sway;

And the festival should bring in,

All our Gladness on display!


This is a decree to observe,

This, the ordinance of our God,

God of Israel, God of Jacob,

After He fought for you.  Oh-oh—

God established this new rule

When against Egyptians blew;

As for Joseph, his descendants,

Celebrate the truest God.

Then, I heard an unknown voice:

"I removed the weight that was hoist

On their shoulders, from their shoulders;

Setting free their hands.  Oh-oh—

They were freed from overloads.

From their quota, from their ropes,

When you called on Me, I listened;

~~Then, I~~ *Then, I* Saved in thundershows!


At the bitters of Meribah,

There, I tested you for My awe;

Hear my warning, all my people,—

If you would listen now! Oh-oh—

*Never* ~~Israel~~, take ~~no~~ *a* foreign god

In among you, ~~never shroud~~. *don't applaud.*

Do not worship any other:

I alone Am God., *your God.*


And forever, I Am your God,

Freed from Egypt, I brought you up.

Open wide your mouth, I'll fill it,

Open wide your mouth!  Oh-oh—

"But my people closed their ears

Would not listen, would not hear.

Israel would not, would not, would not!

They would not come near. *to hear.*

When I saw they meant their goodbye,

   Then I gave them over to lies

Then they followed their contrivances,

   Making faulty wiles. Oh-oh!

    "If My people only came

      Near to Me to hear again,

   Oh, if only Israel followed

~~For,~~ My better way is plain!


See how quickly I would subdue

   All oppressors over you,

Turn My hand against your enemies

   All who hate the LORD!  Oh-oh!

   They would cringe before My hand,

    Yet their punishment would stand.

   You, beloved, I ~~replenish with~~ *would feed you*

   ~~Finest~~ Honey wheat. ~~From~~ *from finest lands."*

# Psalm 83

(A psalm of Alarm by Asaph)
*TUNE: O COME, ALL YE FAITHFUL*
*ADESTE FIDELES*, uncertain. Possibly John Reading (c. 1645–1692) or
King John IV of Portugal (c. 1650) or John Francis Wade (1711–1786) who signed and published it.

Oh, do not keep silent, God, do not keep silent!

Do not resolve to hold your peace, Highest God!

Do You hear the uproar that Your foes are making?

They raise their heads against You,

They lay their crafty plans out

Against your hidden people; they're plotting as one.


They say, "Come together, let us wipe them all out:

The nation of Israel be remembered no more!"

The tent homes of Edom make their covenant with

The Ishmaelites and Moab,

The Hagrites and Philistia

With Amalek and Ammon, and Assur and Lot.


So do to these nations as you did to Midian,

To Sisera and Jabin at the banks of Kishon.

For they became dung for fertilizing Endor;

Oh, make their nobles like them:

The princes of Zalmunna

And Oreb, Zeeb and Zebah who've invaded Your lands.

My God, make the raiders, claiming God's good homelands,

Stubble and tumbleweeds before whirling wind.

Consume them with fire, in the woods and mountains.

May You pursue their lot with

The blazing flame and tempest

And terrify the lot of them in Your hurricane!


Pour shame on their visage, as they turn to view You,

In shame, may they see Your name in banners, oh LORD.

Let foes be dismayed and perishing forever;

Let their disgrace be telling

That You are Most Compelling;

They rose against the LORD, whose name is over the earth.

# PSALM 84

(Praise for Recitude and Peace in God's House)
*TUNE: JOYFUL, JOYFUL, WE ADORE THEE*
"*Hymn to Joy,*" from the 9th Symphony of Ludwig van Beethoven,
(1824); adapted by Edward Hodges,
*Alternate Tune: I WILL SING THE WONDROUS STORY OF THE CHRIST OF CALVARY,*
*Hyfrydol,*
by Rowland H. Prichard (1830)

Oh, how lovely is your Temple,

Splendid King, resplendent LORD!

And I long, yes, faint with longing

For a footstep near Your courts.

See I am coming into His courtyard

By the Living God, received;

Even swallows and young sparrows

Nest in welcome, nest in peace.


Here among your holy altars,

There they nest and have their young,

Commandeering Angel armies,

You're my King and You're my God!

Listen, 'hear the happy birdsong;

They accompany Your praise!

With the ones who live in worship,

Altogether, songs they raise.

O how happy are the strong ones
Of the LORD, who walk with You,
Those who want beyond temptations
To be true and follow through.
When they walk through Rifts of Weeping,
Ancient springs become their rest
In transforming pools of blessing
Rains collected to refresh!

In their rectitude of strength, they
Come to meet our Mercy Shield:
He's the Lord in Zion's high court;
Our Defender and our seal.
You are YAHWEH, the Almighty!
O Most High, so near and fair!
Listen to Your own Anointed,
Israel's God, let all take care!

Show Your kindness, Your compassion,

For Your mercy covers shame.

And a single day in worship

Betters any thousand days!

I would rather be a doorman

For the worshipers of God

Than to live in gaudy mansions

And wherever You are not.


For the Light of YAHWEH's brilliance,

Like the sun and like a shield:

He Protects our steady passage;

He provides exquisite fields.

No good thing is He withholding

From all those who walk His path!

This, the Lord of angel armies,

Shelters those of truthfulness.

# Psalm 85

*(For the director of music. Thoughts of the Sons of Korah)*
*TUNE: AMAZING GRACE*
Unknown. "*NEW BRITAIN*" (1835)

Oh LORD, You've shown Your pleasure here,

Your land and wealth restored!

With Jacob's good repute and joy

Our sins have been transferred!


You set aside Your wrath in full

And turned from fierce intent,

Restoring us, our Savior God,

Erasing our offense!


Shall judgment run forever strong?

Shall generations waste?

You shall revive us once again

So let Your people praise!


LORD, show unfailing love to us

Oh, grant salvation true!

I'll bear Your peace and serve in faith

For God is all virtue.

He promised peace to all his own,
His faithful servants raised!
Oh, keep them from their foolish ways,
All those whom reverence saved.

So generations rest in God,
While Love and Faith lock hands.
When Peace and Right embrace and kiss,
His glory shares our land!

True Faith springs from the barren earth,
The just look down from heav'n.
We've learned the LORD gives good always,
For Eden thrives again.

He leads with honesty ahead;
His feet prepare the way;
He steps in right, in good, in peace;
We follow and obey.

# PSALM 93

TUNE: *THE FIRST NOEL*
of Cornish origin, it was first published in
Carols Ancient and Modern (1823)

The LORD! He reigns in majesty!

His reign is established in robes of strength!

    And armed in majesty this world

    Was also secured by His strength unfurled.

How long ago You guaranteed,

    You are reigning enthroned from eternity!


The seas, oh LORD, have lifted their throats,

The seas lifted up their thundering voice!

    The seas have pounded volleying waves,

    With a might never seen on the oceans that break!

Though mightier than the breakers at sea—

    Is the reign of the LORD breaking higher and free!


Your statutes, LORD, Your statutes do stand;

Your statutes stand firmly presiding Your hand.

    In holiness, Your house is adorned

    Forever in days, holiness will perform.

Your statutes, LORD, Your statutes stand firm!

    And holiness graces Your home and Your word!

# PSALM 94

(Proclamation-Declaration to God and to Fools)

*Tune: I WONDER AS I WANDER*
John Jacob Niles (1933)
*Alternate Tunes:* IMMORTAL, INVISIBLE GOD ONLY WISE
Orig. St. Denio, Welsh melody, from Canaidau y Cyssegr,
by John Roberts (1839)
*AWAY IN A MANGER*
Mueller, James R. Murray (1887)
This song will be most effective when all three tunes are used to interpret various verses.

The LORD is a God who avenges His own.

    Oh, God my avenger, appear and shine on!

Rise up, Judge of earth's haughty; rise and repay

The lot they deserve, LORD, how long till that day?


The wicked are jubilant, arrogant rogues;

    How long will they pour out their arrogant words?

The doers of evil are boasting their game.

They're crushing your people, LORD; widows are slain!


They murder the fatherless, pressing the poor,

    Run through Your inheritance, saying, "The LORD

Is taking no notice, our God does not see;"

Take notice, you foolish ones! Look now, and see!


You, fools among people; you fools should wise up!

    Does He who has fashioned your ears not hear much?

Does He who forms eyes and designs not see true?

Does He punish nations and not punish you?

Does this One who teaches man lack any thought?

    The LORD knows the plans you make all come to naught;

How blessed the one whom You discipline, LORD,

How blessed the one whom You teach from your law!

 

You grant us relief from the troubles we're thrown,

    The LORD won't reject or abandon His own;

Till a pit is dug for the wicked to lay.

He'll never forsake his own righteous ones' day.

 

Take courage for judgment will soon run upright,

    and all who believe it are also upright.

Oh, who will rise up for me against the vile?

Oh, who will stand and pledge against their guile?

 

Unless the LORD had provided me help,

    I soon would have ended in silence of death.

But When I admitted, "My footstep had slipped,"

Your unfailing love, LORD, supported me then.

 

When cares were abounding, LORD, You brought me joy.

    When anxious, Your great consolation deployed!

But, how can a throne so corrupt be allied

with You— for this throne brings despair codified?

They banded together against righteous ones

    Condemning the innocent till they succumbed.

The LORD has become my fort and my rescue.

And I hide in God for the rock of refuge.


Oh, He will repay evildoers for sins;

    And He will destroy them for their wickedness;

The LORD will destroy them, for He is our God.

My confidence rests in the cleft of the Rock.

# PSALM 95

(Call to Worship)

*Tune: O, HOLY NIGHT*

*Adolphe Adams (1847)*

Come, let us shout; make joyful noise to our LORD,

in triumph shout to our refuge and rock!

Come, let us enter His presence with thanksgiving;

And, let us shout to Him in a victor's song.

The LORD is a great God, above all rulers,

All the depths of earth are in His hand,

All mountain peaks are His, He made them rise up.

The sea is His; for He formed it with His hands;

Oh, come, let us worship our Maker and bow down.


We kneel before the LORD our God our Maker,

We are the sheep and the people of His hand,

If you can hear, His voice today is calling;

Do not repeat hardened hearts at Meribah.

As on that day at Massah in the wild

Where your ancestors tested Me and tried;

Though they had seen the wonders that I did there.

Then, I despised those hearts for forty years,

They never~ entered My rest~ in all their years.


Then, I despised those hearts~ that went astray.

I swore in My anger, "They do~ not know My ways."

I swore in My anger, "They do~ not know My ways."

# PSALM 96

(Call to Worship and Praise)
*Tune: I SAW THREE SHIPS*
Arr. of *Greensleeves*,17th century, possibly Derbyshire,
also published by William Sandys in 1833.

Oh, sing a novel song to God;

   Proclaim His name, proclaim His name!

Come all the earth to praise the LORD;

For saving grace every morning!


Praise the LORD, His saving name;

   Declare his deeds, declare his deeds!

His glory through all nations,

And all the races wonder!


The LORD is great and greatly feared

   Above all gods, above all gods!

Our God is worthy of His praise

Above the nations' idols.


The LORD made every heaven,

   In splendor, in splendor

Before Him, strength and majesty

In sanctuary of glory.

Ascribe to God, the families
    Of nations, of nations,
The strength and glory due His name;
Ascribe, and bring an offering.

O come into His courts with fear,
    O worship Him, O worship Him!
The Lord in holy splendor;
And tremble, all of the earth!

Proclaim among the nations:
    "The Lord reigns, the Lord reigns!"
The world is firmly set in stone,
And it shall never be toppled!

The Lord will judge humanity
    With equity, with equity!
Oh, let the earth be glad to sing
And heavens filled with rejoicing!

Let all the sea resound in song
    And all within, and all within!
And, let the fields be jubilant,
And everything within them!

Let all the trees rejoice and praise;

   The forests sing, the forests sing!

Let all creation now rejoice

Before the LORD who is coming!


He comes to judge the earth complete

   In righteousness, in righteousness!

So, He will judge humanity

In faithfulness the world-wide!

# PSALM 98

(Call to Rejoice in God's Faithfulness and Righteous Judgment)

*TUNE: THE HOLLY AND THE IVY*
collected by Cecil Sharp, by Mary Clayton of Chipping Campden (1909)

or French carol: Il Est Ne (He is Born)
Or, French Carol: Entre le bœuf et l'âne gris (Between the Ox and Gray Donkey)

Sing to the LORD a new song,                            -set quiet tone with Il Est Ne

 The marvels He has done;

His right hand, His holy arm

 Have worked His salvation.


The LORD designed salvation,                            -start The Holly and the Ivy

 He's known to every land

And revealed his righteousness to us,

 To the world and all nations.


He has remembered Israel

 With faithfulness and love;

All inhabitants on earth have seen

 The salvation of our God.


Shout in your joy to Yahweh,

 May all the earth be glad,

Bursting into Jubal's song of praise

 Making music to the LORD.

Now with the harp and singing,
   With trumpets blasting rings
The bellows of the ram's horn—
   Shout for joy before this King.

The seas resound like big bands,
   Drumming everything to sand,
With the world, and all who live in it.
   Let the rivers clap their hands.

Let the mountains sing together;
   Sing with joy before the LORD,
For he comes to judge the world's decrees.
   His righteousness restored.

The LORD will judge all races              -Il Est Ne v. 1
   Not with sleight of hand or bribe,
Not with human minds or human laws
   But with fairness He decides.

# PSALM 116

(The Rushing Exaltation of Someone Rescued from Imminent Death)

*TUNE: JOY TO THE WORLD!*
First published in 1719 in Isaac Watts' English collection;
*The Psalms of David, though the tune was applied to Psalm 98*

I love the LORD, He heard my voice;

   He heard my cry for love!

Because He turned to me,

   To listen, I will call on Him

      As long as I have breath,

      As long as I have breath,

      As long as mercy beats in my chest!


Cords of death became a web!

   The anguish of the grave

Rolled over me in sorrow,

   Came over me to strangle;

      Then I called to the LORD:

      The name by which I'm saved,

      "Oh, save me! LORD, save me!" I called His name!

Gracious and righteous is the LORD!

    Our God is full of love!

The LORD protects the simple;

    I know for I was simple!

        I was brought low, but He

        Saved with His tender love,

        He lifted compassion, and mercy up!


My soul, return to your sweet rest;

    The LORD has been your good!

For you, oh LORD, have rescued,

    Delivered me from sorrow,

        From weeping tears of death,

        Where I stumbled without breath,

        You purpose my lively walk before the LORD!


Though I cried, I trusted God,

    I trusted in the LORD!

Then  I cried in alarming notes,

    "See my affliction rises up!

        From liars, everyone!

        From liars, everyone!"

        What shall I return to God for all His good?

I will lift up His saving cup

    And call the LORD by name!

I will fulfill my vows to Him

    With all His people watching.

        The LORD sees the last breath

        Of his faithful servants' deaths

        As precious, yes precious, in His sight!


Truly I am your servant, LORD;

    I serve as I was taught;

 You rescued, and You freed me,

    From chains and my undoing.

        An offering full of thanks

        Oh LORD, to You I bring,

        Fulfilling my vows to You In Your great name!


"Oh, Hallelujah to the LORD—!"

    In courtyards of His own!

The presence of His holy ones,

    The houses of Jerusalem,

        Will bring the LORD His praise,

        When all together raise,

        Oh, praise Him, the LORD OF ALL, Jerusalem!

# PSALM 119 ׀ Waw

(Shameless trust in following God's Mandates)

*TUNE: ANGELS FROM THE REALMS OF GLORY*
Irish, James Montgomery (1816)

Come include me in Your mercies:

Your salvation by Your word.

Then will I have answers for him

Who rebuffs me with his slurs.

I am trusting, ever trusting,

May Your word of truth be mine!


All in Godly hope of order

Shall I keep Your mandates' rule

And continually obey them,

Evermore for they are Yours.

And because I'm walking with You,

I will walk at liberty!


Since I seek Your doctrines daily,

I will freely speak Your rules.

Listen to my testimonies,

Bejeweled kings will be in school;

I will never

Be ashamed there.

For I love all Your commands!

I delight myself in searching

Your commandments, which I love.

I will also lift my hands up

To Your dictates from above!

Meditating

On Your statutes

I am loving all your plans!

# PSALM 119 ז Zayin

(Conversational Testimony with God about walking in His Word/Law)
*Tune: WHILE SHEPHERDS WATCHED THEIR FLOCKS BY NIGHT*
"Siroe," an opera by George Frederick Handel (1728)

Remember all the words You gave

To this Your servant, waiting?

For with these promises You spoke

And caused in me great hope.

This *is* my comfort now.


In my affliction, Your word came

And brought to me new life.

The proud deride me with abuse

*Yet* Your word has arrived.

I will defend Your law.


Remembering Your ancient paths,

And judgments, LORD, of old,

I've comforted myself with them,

While umbrage took ahold,

Against the wicked world.


Your statutes have become my songs

In pilgrim's homes, in awe.

In the night Your greatness comes to mind

Oh LORD, I keep Your law.

This road has made it mine!

# PSALM 144

(Conversational Worship, Prayer and Meditation on the Complete Defense,
Peace and Bounty of God)
*TUNE: COME THOU LONG EXPECTED JESUS*
Hyfrydol, Rowland H. Prichard, (1830)

Safe and solid, my high mountain,

God who trains me fair and well;

He's my bedrock and high tower

His command will surely prevail.

And, I wonder why you love me,

Why you bother to rise to my prayer?

Surely human beings are merely

Shadows in the smoky air.


Stepping out of your highest heaven

Spark volcanoes in this earth

Hurl your lightning all directions

Shoot your arrows from your hearth!

Armor reaches from this expanse to sea

Pull me out of this ocean of hate.

Loosen the grip of those lawless and lying,

Scheming traitors with knives in wait.

God-Commander, who rescued David

Let me play a worthy tune,

How you rescued me from danger

I will raise my praise to You.

Now I recognize my Savior

I have been introduced to the Truth.

Make Your oaks from innocent children:

Sprawling shade in a lovely muse.


Then our barns will fill with plenty

Every preparation supplied.

Herds of sheep and cattle grazing,

All this plenty You provide;

No more breaching of our limits,

Tears and crime are both done away.

No more enslaving, deriding, defiling,

Safely trusting the One, Yahweh.

## PSALM 147

(Praising the sustaining power and sovereignty of the LORD)
*TUNE: GOD REST YE MERRY GENTLEMEN*
Orig. English folk song collected by William B. Sandys (1833)
Or, French Carol Il Est Ne (He is Born)

Sing Hallelujah! Praise the LORD!

How good it is to sing!

All praises to our God, the LORD;

Delightful and fitting

To praise the LORD who builds us up,

To build Jerusalem;

For the exiled He gathers back

To Israel, back to Him,

Healing broken hearts and binding up their wounds!


The LORD determines heaven's lights:

Appoints and numbers stars.

He calls them each by their own name,

Our LORD is great in power!

His understanding has no cap,

Or limits to His might.

He sustains every humble soul

But casts the evil out

Oh, He bounces wicked out upon the ground.

Sing to the LORD with grateful praise;

Make music to our God

Come with the harp and strike the strings;

With gratefulness applaud!

This God, He covers sky with clouds

And He supplies the rain

Making grass grow for herds upon the hills,

Providing grain,

For the cattle and the squalling little birds.


His pleasure is not in the strength

Of horses' speed or force,

Nor His delight in warriors' mighty

Legs that run in war;

The LORD delights in those who fear Him

As the Holy One,

Those who put their entire hope

In His unfailing love.

Praise the LORD, extol your God, Jerusalem!

He strengthens bars defending

All your gates, Jerusalem,

And blesses all your people

In your borders with His calm.

He satisfies you with the finest

Wheat for all to eat,

Sending His words and His commands;

To all the earth replete,

And the snow spreads like wool and frosty sleet.


He hurls down hail like pebbles;

Who can stop His icy blasts?

He melts the ice with His command;

And storms so waters dance.

He gave His law to Jacob

And to Israel by His word.

He did not give it to the other nations

Of the world.

Singing, Hallelujah! Praise the Sovereign LORD.

# PSALM 149

(Joy and Praise in God for Crowning the Humble with Victory)
*TUNE: SING THE WONDROUS LOVE OF JESUS*
(When We all Get To Heaven, What a Day of Rejoicing that Will Be!)
By, Emily D. Wilson (1898)
*Alternate Tune: I WILL SING THE WONDROUS STORY*
by, Peter P. Bilhorn, 1886,
*Alternate Tune: JOYFUL, JOYFUL WE ADORE THEE*
(Beethovan)

Praise the LORD and sing a new song!

    Raise His praise in band and choir.

Singing groups of faithful ones, oh,

    Praise your Maker, where you are!

All in Zion, all in Israel,

All His children, praise your King!

Joy is rising, exultations,

Let them praise His name with strings.


Dance and praise the LORD together,

    Tambourine, and harp, and drums!

Praise the LORD with joyful dancing,

    He delights in faithful ones;

How He crowns the meek with glory,

He will crown the humble heads!

Let's begin the celebration;

God rewards and honors them.

Let them sing and sing ~~again~~ for joy as

      They are lying ~~down upon~~ on their beds.

Let the praises of their God ring

      In their mouth and in their heads!

With a sharpened sword in hand they —

Excise all the world of wrong.

Punish all the wicked nations

Hurling swords at noble wrongs.


These, their leaders wielding chains of iron,

      ~~Wielding iron~~ over lackeys' lives,

Execute the judgment written

      Over deputies alike.

This is how the glorious privilege

Of His faithful ones will fare.

Praise the LORD, ~~sharing~~ He showers glory

With His faithful everywhere!

THIS BOOK IS AN INTERACTIVE, DYNAMIC WORD. Interact with us about it!
https://www.facebook.com/PsalmHymns.Larkins/?ref=bookmarks

## PLEASE VISIT US AT:

http://CaptureBookstore.com or
http://CaptureMeBooks.com
for our other book selections
Including the full Psalm-Hymns collection!

IF YOU LIKE ANY OF

THE POETIC LYRICS,

WE'D LOVE TO HEAR

*HOW* YOU USED THEM

OR HOW THEY SPOKE

TO YOU!

Sharing a book or writing an

honest review are the finest

compliments you can give to

an author!

CPSIA information can be obtained
at www.ICGtesting.com
Printed in the USA
FFOW01n1115011017
40576FF